To David

Shine your Gifts

THE SEVEN GIFTS

A Story

The Guiding Message of Nature

Dr. Marty Finkelstein

Love you,

Marty

This book is a work of fiction. Any resemblance to actual events or persons, living or dead, is entirely coincidental.

"The Seven Gifts," by Dr. Marty Finkelstein. ISBN 978-1-60264-602-5 (softcover); 978-1-60264-603-2 (ebook).

Published 2010 by Virtualbookworm.com Publishing Inc., P.O. Box 9949, College Station, TX 77842, US.

Manufactured in the United States of America.

ACKNOWLEDGMENTS

Thank you Janna Zonder for her guided editing, engaging conversations, and wonderful friendship.

Thank you to my children, Julia and Nathaniel, whose wisdom and love inspire me, and who give me the joy and blessing of being a dad.

Thank you to my sweetheart, Julie Austin, whose love brings me deep into the ocean, lifts me up toward the mountain, and sky. I am your greatest fan.

In every creation, there are always so many people who add to the color and creative spirit of my life. Thank you.

And to the seven gifts who remind me that each day is a miracle, and are here to guide us through our journey of life. Thank you!

Contents

FOREWORD

Dr. Marty Finkelstein's *The Seven Gifts* takes us on a personal journey through the eyes of the seeker. His approach is very holistic and mesmerizing. From the very beginning he captures the attention of the reader, as they become one with the seeker. One quickly realizes that he is allowing us a glimpse into his own life. The messages and lessons are profound, educational, and at times can leave you gasping for air. The author encourages self discovery through silence, retrospection, and the guidance of *The Seven Gifts* of nature. It is a beautiful emotional ride on a roller coaster of life. *The Seven Gifts* is a powerful and life changing resource that belongs on every book shelf and in every library. It is an easy read and a timeless gift that will enable the reader to affect positive and life long changes in their lives.

Belinda M. Stinson-Head, PhD
President/CEO, AAH Learning & Consulting

INTRODUCTION

This story began as he asked for guidance.

Sitting facing the morning sun, knowing that his vacation would soon end, he felt a deep dread and hopelessness welling up inside him. He would have to return to working, paying bills, and the multitude of daily stresses that now seemed to define his life.

His name is of little consequence, for he is the seeker in each of us who yearns for answers, peacefulness, aliveness and enlightenment.

Perhaps like the seeker, you have tried hard to follow the right path. You have enriched your life with religious teachings, you have read hundreds of inspirational books and attended countless seminars that left you excited, turned on, and born again with renewed possibilities.

But then life hit like a forceful wave that knocked you off course and once again, you were left struggling to understand where you went wrong, or which direction you should take next. Perhaps those of you who have lived longer than forty years thought experience alone would bring wisdom and peace of mind. Maybe you thought that knowledge would satisfy your thirst for life. Or, your career, family and friends would fill the empty spaces in your heart.

Of course, there was always true love to get us through the rough spots, wasn't there? So many of us believed that love would fulfill our every wish and desire. But, we discovered that even love could not ease the anxiety that accompanied us to bed like a faithful companion and greeted us each morning, unsettling our spirits with doubt, fear and sadness.

This story may be your story. As you read it, I invite you to insert your name wherever it feels appropriate.

* * * * *

As he sat in quiet solitude with the morning sun warming his face, the seeker asked for guidance. Immediately, a dear friend's words echoed in his mind. *You have done everything right. You have worked hard, raised a beautiful family, served others each day, and shared life's wisdom through your teaching and healing. While I have been a vagabond, traveling the world with little resources other than my KNOWING, and sadly, I see you suffering.*

Recalling his friend's words brought despair to the seeker's heart. He had been so certain the discoveries he had made as a young man would be enough to guide him throughout his life. His youth had exploded with a vastness of rich experiences. He was sure life would be abundant and rewarding. He would fulfill his own dreams by assisting others to see and discover the healing light within themselves.

As you are reading this, do you remember the promises you made to yourself when you were young? Do you feel as if something is missing? Does it seem that you are searching for happiness and love, but each step forward gives you only a brief taste of bliss before it disappears?

When we are young, we are filled with dreams. Even our mistakes and misfortunes can be chalked up to the inexperience of youth. But, what about those of us who are older now and looking back? When did the dreams stop? Where did our youth go? Why did the knowledge that ***ANYTHING IS POSSIBLE, EVERYTHING WILL WORK OUT,*** *quietly vanish from our minds without so much as a farewell?*

Can you hear the paradox? That knowledge isn't lost! Lying dormant within you are all the insights you discovered when you were young. Yet there is more. You now have the clarity of perspective that only experience brings. Like the seeker in this story, you are ready to reconnect to what you already know.

All the lessons, all the sermons and books, the seminars, the challenges and excitement are ready to be awakened again within you. But, like the caterpillar, you must allow the natural process of metamorphosis to occur before you can manifest into the extraordinary beauty of the butterfly.

Inside, you know who you are. You are Spirit, seasoned by time! Everything within you is ready to blossom, like the tree of knowledge or the sacred lotus. Listen to the wondrous teachings of nature. God is calling you to enlightenment.

THE FIRST GIFT
THE EARTH
THE FOUNDATION, THE SOURCE

From the earth

Life gives birth

The fertile ground

The ancestral sound

Tilled and plowed with compassion

And love

Comes forth what life is made of

Below your feet

Feel it speak

Believe in the messages

That you seek

WHAT IS IT YOU WANT?

Guidance.
I feel lost and disconnected from you.
I feel I am not hearing you.
Not as clearly as I once did.
Maybe not at all.

WHY DO YOU THINK YOU STOPPED LISTENING?

I did not realize it at first.
Initially I felt I was doing YOUR WORK.
Then, it slowly seemed to become just work.
At first, I felt I was LIVING LIFE.
And, then it became making a living.

WHY DO YOU THINK YOU STOPPED LIVING LIFE?

Fear, worries, anxieties.
Everything seemed to close in, rather than expand.
I lost the power of my faith.
I lost the passion for action.
My words failed me.

THAT IS WHAT IT FELT LIKE TO YOU?

Yes!

AND WHAT DID IT FEEL LIKE BEFORE, WHEN YOU WERE LIVING YOUR LIFE?

Listening and feeling
Experiencing with an open heart.
Dancing and singing, joyfully.
Learning for the sake of learning
And, loving for the sake of loving.
No strings attached, with no expectations.

SO, THERE YOU HAVE IT. YOU ALREADY KNOW!

If I already knew, I would not be hurting right now.

IT IS GOOD YOU RECOGNIZE YOUR PAIN.

Oh, I definitely feel my pain.

SO WHAT IS IT YOU WANT NOW?

I want to tune into you.
I want to raise my listening IQ.
So that I feel you in my mind, body and spirit each moment.
I want to keep my youthful promises with myself
And expand my divine relationship with you.

WALK WITH ME.

Absolutely . . .

TAKE YOUR SHOES OFF AS YOU WALK THROUGH THE WOODS. CAN YOU FEEL THE EARTH BELOW YOU WITH EACH STEP? CLOSE YOUR EYES AND LISTEN. SAY NOTHING.

As he walked, the seeker could feel the earth's force vibrating beneath his feet. He had asked for guidance, and now he embraced his own responsibility to listen and trust. Everything grew out from the earth.

THE EARTH IS THE FOUNDATION. THE PAST, THIS MOMENT, AND THE FUTURE ARE HELD IN ITS FERTILE SOIL. CAN YOU FEEL THE EARTH THAT IS INSIDE YOU? THAT IS YOU?

As he continued to walk, he soon observed that he could not tell where the earth and his body were separated. They were one. There was no distinction between his feet and the ground. His roots sank deep into the earth's core, anchoring him, so that, like a magnificent tree, he could stretch towards heaven. He felt intensely alive.

FEEL THE PRESENCE OF THE EARTH WITHIN YOU. IT HOLDS EVERY MEMORY. IT HOLDS EVERY BELIEF. IT HOLDS EVERY CHOICE, DREAM, ANSWER AND EVERY POSSIBILITY. AT ITS CORE BURNS THE INTERNAL PURE FIRE OF CONSCIOUSNESS AND INFINITE WISDOM.

He began to remember when the earth inside him had felt alive and fertile for growing. He remembered when he had shaken loose from the past, willing himself to face challenges with faith and courage. It was clear his inner earth had been neglected. How easy it had been to forget to water or feed that precious soil.

What are you feeling right now? Do you feel the memories in your earth? The fears, the joys, the wounds, the love? Do you see the stories written there - the ones you've shared, as well as the ones that have been buried deep in your core? What about the stories you have tried to forget, yet they scratch against your heart like thorns breaking through the earth's crust, clawing against you, influencing your every thought and action?

If you are able, walk barefoot outside today on your lawn, or the beach, or the woods. Can you feel the earth touch you as you reclaim your connection and oneness with it? You are the source. The earth is not separate from you. Now is the time to reclaim your true essence from the earth. Regardless of the past, as remarkable as it might seem, you are reborn with each step.

THE SECOND GIFT
THE SEEDS
THE CREATIVE FIRE

The seed holds the creative spark

Into the light, out from the dark

Life forms in every design

In everything that is living

And every thought in our mind

Anything imaginable and every possibility

Everything we dream of

And everything we see

Is the birth of the seeds to create life's destiny

WHAT DID THE EARTH SHARE WITH YOU?

The earth reminded me of my true essence.

AND WHAT IS YOUR TRUE ESSENCE?

Feeling and being connected to the foundation of my spirit.

AND WHAT DOES THAT MEAN TO YOU?

Knowing when beliefs are not empowering the life I want to create.
Being conscious when feelings of failure are hardening my spirit, and my own soil.
Being reminded that my creative spirit wants to flourish and feel alive.

SO YOU FEEL YOU ARE RECEIVING GUIDANCE?

Yes indeed!

ARE YOU CERTAIN YOU WANT FURTHER GUIDANCE? ARE YOU READY TO ALLOW LIFE TO BLOSSOM, WHILE WALKING COURAGEOUSLY INTO THE UNKNOWN?

The simple answer was yes - yet, the seeker felt his body contract as the question was met with hesitation. The unknown, what did that mean? He immediately thought of the story of Abraham and Isaac. Abraham sacrificing his son never felt comfortable to the seeker. The ultimate sacrifice to prove one's worthiness was a spiritual game of faith he wasn't up for. Maybe he was in over his head.

YOU ARE STRUGGLING.

Yes!

TRUST IN THE GOD YOU KNOW IN YOUR SPIRIT AND ALLOW ITS VOICE TO BE HEARD.

There was silence . . .

YOU ARE READY FOR YOUR SECOND GIFT.

I still feel anxious.

YOU ARE READY FOR YOUR SECOND GIFT.

As he walked around a bend in the woods, he came upon a beautiful wild garden full of exotic flowers whose blossoms reached toward the sky. There he witnessed vines and trees that held magnificent edible fruits and vegetables sparkling with life. It looked the way he thought paradise would look and the sensuous aroma seemed to lift the heaviness from his body. Where are we?

PARADISE

But, really, where are we?

LET GO AND BE GUIDED BY YOUR EXPERIENCE. OPEN YOUR EYES WIDE. LOOK AT THE DIVERSE EXPRESSIONS OF LIFE. FEEL AND SEE THE CREATIVE FORCE BEFORE YOU. BE GUIDED BY THE SEEDS THAT GROW FROM THE EARTH.

The seeker was overwhelmed, swept away by the magnificence of the colors, the shapes, the distinct textures of each flower. As he breathed in the fragrance that permeated the air, he felt inspired and transported. Everything was alive. It was as if he had gazed into a magical mirror. The creative force of life reflected back the divine spark of creation that lived within him.

Can you feel the seeds lying dormant within you? Are they being fed and watered? Are they nurtured so that they will blossom and fulfill your dreams? Can you still imagine what is possible for your life? So many amazing, creative, talented, intelligent people, who started out with adventurous visions and sometimes nothing more than their faith and passion, now feel trapped in their middle-aged lives. They've come to believe dreams are only for the young and innocent. Responsibility has replaced courageousness. Comfort has replaced freedom, and compromise has replaced aliveness.

You may be thinking: What's wrong with responsibility, being comfortable, or compromising when necessary? Nothing is inherently wrong, but perhaps you - like the seeker - have become more accustomed to talking about aliveness and higher consciousness, than actually being alive and conscious.

Deeply intoxicated by the beauty around him, the seeker's legs began to wobble. He sat upon the ground and drifted into a deep meditation. Every seed was an expression of life and he was bearing witness to God's glorious creations. He felt the seeds of life dancing inside him. Every cell within him held the vibration of a divine wisdom waiting to manifest, wanting to be born. He realized he was here to create, to fully express and imagine beyond his wildest dreams, the true colors and nuance of his being. Every thought held the potential for magic, for sacredness, for miracles to occur - whether it was the birthing of an infant or a sacred vision, the garden of his soul required mindful tending.

As you are reading this, reflect upon your own life. When were the times you felt most creative? What possibilities occurred to you out of your creative energy? How did you feel about yourself when you were being creative? How did your body feel? Were you happy? Did your loved ones notice a difference in your attitude? How is it different when you are not expressing your creativity? What are some of the reasons for not being creative in your life at the present time? When we are aware of the creative force that runs through all of life, our own creativity blossoms in ways that will astound us. We have only to open our minds and hearts to the creative force that dwells within each one of us.

After the seeker emerged from his meditation, he felt calm and at peace. Although he had always enjoyed the gifts of nature, he had never before listened to the subtle voice of guidance that it offered. He had appreciated the magnificent beauty that existed *outside* him, but he had never known that same splendor was *within* him just waiting to be expressed in the form of his own creative purpose.

CAN YOU FEEL YOUR BODY?

Yes!

CONTINUE TO LISTEN TO YOUR BODY. AS WE WALK AGAIN, BEGIN TO FEEL YOUR ABDOMEN.

The seeker felt immediately afraid. He didn't understand why, but a tight knot formed within his stomach and he lost the peaceful feeling he had just experienced.

ARE YOU WILLING TO LET GO AND CHANGE?

I thought I was, but right now I feel uncomfortable.

AND HOW DOES THAT FEEL?

I'm afraid of the unknown again. Something feels blocked and distrusting. Tense. This is not simple. This is not easy.

WHAT IS NOT SIMPLE?

Life. I want it to be simple. I want the answers to be simple, but they are not. One moment everything feels great and then the next moment, I'm obstructed and in pain again.

MAKE A VERY TIGHT FIST.

The seeker closed his hand into a fist.

KEEP YOUR HAND CLOSED. EVEN WHEN I TELL YOU TO OPEN YOUR HAND, KEEP IT CLOSED.

Okay . . .

OPEN YOUR HAND!

He kept his fist closed.

NOW THIS TIME WHEN I TELL YOU TO OPEN YOUR HAND, OPEN IT.

Okay . . .

OPEN YOUR HAND.

He opened his fist and relaxed his hand.

WHICH WAS EASIER FOR YOU, KEEPING YOUR FIST CLOSED OR OPENING YOUR HAND?

Neither one felt particularly harder or easier. They felt about the same.

SO BE IT! YOU GET TO CHOOSE.

THE THIRD GIFT
THE RIVER
THE GIFT OF CHANGE AND TRUST

The river's current flows downstream

A cleansing force that renews our dreams

Along the banks between mountains flow

The gift of change where we can grow

The unpredictable river steady and true

Alters the landscape as waters run through

With symphony's sounds and cleansing stream

Changing each moment, fulfilling our dreams

Nature's rocks and trees along the way

Can shift the meandering course each day

Yet from the beginning of time long ago

The river keeps changing, continues to flow.

ARE YOU READY TO LET GO?

I thought I was.

THERE ARE MANY STAGES TO BEING BORN.

Just when I thought I had received the guidance I needed . . .

YOU THOUGHT YOU WERE DONE?

Now I feel anxious again.

THAT IS WHY WE ARE HERE.

Where?

WALK AND LISTEN.

As the seeker walked through the woods, he was drawn in the direction of a symphony of water that danced off rocks and lapped the shore. Through the dense foliage, he saw a crystal clear rippling river. The pure air was alive and the sound was hypnotic. He smiled and breathed deeply, feeling his lungs expand with life.

WHAT DO YOU OBSERVE WHEN YOU LOOK AT THE RIVER?

It is beautiful and feels alive.

WHAT ELSE?

It's sparkling, clear and looks deliciously cool.

WHAT ELSE?

It is moving and self-cleansing as it meanders over and around and between the obstacles in its path.

AND WHAT IF OBSTACLES BLOCK IT FROM MOVING?

It would interfere with the river's flow and the water would lose its vibrant energy. It would just sit there and begin to die. It would stop being a river.

As the seeker stared into the river, he felt the rhythmic motion of its power being pulled by some invisible force that propelled it forward. The river was on a journey. And, even more importantly, the river seemed determined to get to its destination. He had never thought of a river as being alive before, but it became clear to him that it was alive as long as it kept moving and changing.

WHAT TIME IS THE RIVER?

Excuse me? What time is the river?

WHAT TIME IS THE RIVER?

Do you mean like a time of day - morning, noon or night?

NO. THE TIME OF PAST, PRESENT OR FUTURE.

I guess it is a combination of the past, present and future. A combination of all time.

ARE YOU READY TO DISCOVER THE TIME OF THE RIVER?

How do I discover the time of the river?

BY BECOMING THE RIVER.

So, you want me to meditate on the river or gaze at the river?

NO. I WANT YOU TO JUMP INTO THE RIVER.

I think this is where I begin to question who I am talking to.

TAKE YOUR TIME. NOT EVERYONE IS READY FOR THE RIVER. THE RIVER BRINGS YOU TO THE HEART OF WHO YOU ARE.

As the seeker looked upon the river, he saw its white foaming waters cascading and meandering through a wide channel. He stepped into the cool pool to feel the river's depth, as well as its rocky bottom. He stared into the distance, not knowing what lay beyond the bend in the river. He began to think that asking for guidance might not have been a great idea. He reflected on the spiritual affirmation, "Ask And You Shall Receive." But, he thought, be profoundly clear what you ask for. It may indeed be received.

This looks dangerous!

IT IS DANGEROUS.

Then why do I want to risk my life?

YOU ARE THE ONE WHO SAID YOU WERE DYING.

But, I do not want to be stupid.

THE RIVER IS A POWERFUL MIRROR THAT TEACHES TRUST AND CHANGE. BE

WILLING TO CHANGE AND TRUST. BE UNWILLING TO BE STUPID.

It is hard to know the difference at times.

LET YOURSELF SIT WITH THE RIVER AND REMEMBER THE TIMES YOU HAVE TRUSTED OR RESISTED THE FLOW OF LIFE. FEEL WHEN YOU WERE WILLING TO CHANGE AND LET GO, AND WHEN YOU WERE UNWILLING. WHEN YOU ARE READY TO TRUST THE FLOW OF THE RIVER, JUMP IN. WHEN YOU ARE READY TO TRUST THIS VOICE, JUMP IN. WHEN YOU ARE READY TO LET GO OF THE FEAR, JUMP IN.

What about you? Can you feel the paradox again? What we say we want, and what we are afraid of, are often the same. We want an extraordinary, passionate, loving relationship, but we are afraid to give our love one hundred percent. We want a career that empowers our true desires, yet we are afraid to alter the course of our lives and take risks. We want vibrant health, yet we are unwilling to change our behaviors.

Where in your life are you standing by the banks of the river, contemplating trust and changing your life? Do you want to become more alive, or perhaps feel alive again after a long time? Are you willing to jump? Can you feel the earth inside you shaking loose? Can you feel the seeds inside you longing to blossom creatively?

Do not let fear stop you. Breathe. Allow yourself to feel. Feel your body, feel your thoughts, and feel your emotions. Like the river, your emotions are yearning to let go and be expressed. They have been held back for so long until now. What would you have the seeker do? Remember, this is your story. This is your life. If your fist is closed, are you ready to open it? We all choose . . .

And, then, the seeker let go of his fear and jumped. The gentle force of the dancing waters immediately embraced him. The river was deeper and wider than he thought; yet he felt calm as he awkwardly floated downstream. As the water moved, he moved, as if he were learning to dance for the first time with a passionate partner and teacher. He relaxed and felt the brisk air on his arms. The radiant sun shining through the overhanging branches warmed his face.

As the river meandered around a bend, he felt something shift around him. His dancing partner had decided to dance to a different rhythm, a wilder, less predictable beat. He felt his muscles tighten; his heart raced. He heard himself say, "Listen to the river. This is my guide. She is not here to kill me . . . I HOPE." This would not be a good guide, he thought. He laughed and said out loud, "You're not the evil twin guide, are you?"

His sense of humor had always kicked in when he was nervous or anxious, and now joking felt like a release valve as he realized the danger he might be in. The river seemed to laugh at him as the white water pushed him forward. He spiraled down a steeper slope, occasionally submerging himself beneath the water for seconds longer than he was comfortable. His fear and anxiety escalated.

"I hate these lessons!" he shouted when his head bobbed up and broke the surface of the water. "I get it - Life is unpredictable, be blessed with what you have. That's my lesson. Thank you for being my guide. I'm done now. Did you hear me? I'm DONE!"

But he wasn't, nor was the river. The strong current pulled and pushed him deeper and faster until he began to feel like he was losing it.

Losing his strength.
Losing his fear.
Losing his humor.
Losing his struggle.

He was losing whatever "it" was that he had been holding onto. He experienced a true sense of letting go and being in the present moment. His body continued to pop up, and he would gulp the air unnaturally, before the river slammed him downward and forward again.

During these moments, he observed everything in an instant. His birth, his past, his future, and even the possibility of his death appeared before him as if he were watching a big screen monitor. He saw everything, everything, to the finest details. And, then, even that was gone. Until there was nothing.

What time is the river? Now, the answer was clear. Amazingly clear. The river is now! The time of the river is now! Now….Now….Now….Now…. As he was carried along, he became a molecule of the river in each moment of now. He couldn't explain it, but each moment of now had become timeless and profound. He heard himself say, "now, now," and then he was washed ashore onto a sandy beach.

At that moment, he knew he had chosen not to die, but instead to let go of all attachments that had caused life itself to feel like death. He had chosen to be aware of how to live without the fear of change, of letting go, of letting in, and to consciously welcome life in each moment, knowing that he was not done, and there were still lessons to be learned.

Can you feel the river inside you? Can you feel the obstacles from your past that interfere with the journey of the river that is your life? Think about these obstacles. Can you feel your body contract or expand with each thought, and the feelings that accompany the thoughts? Are you ready to let go and discover the choice embedded in each moment?

THE FOURTH GIFT
THE OCEAN
THE GIFT OF LOVE

The ocean's waves call us deep

In waking hours and in our sleep

Explores the mystery, unveils the unknown

The emotional door to the spirit's home

The depth of the sea reveals what's true

The ocean's heart where love flows through

Only those willing to surrender and explore

Will discover the love never imagined before

It seemed as if the seeker had fallen into a deep sleep, maybe moments or days, he couldn't tell, when he again heard the voice.

WHAT DID THE RIVER SHOW YOU?

The answer to your question: Now is the time.

NOW IS THE TIME!

Why do I get the feeling that I am not done? What more is there to the answer, "Now is the time?"

NOTHING IS MORE AND NOTHING IS LESS, THOUGH THE RIVER HAS TAKEN YOU THROUGH TO THE OTHER SIDE.

The other side of what?

YOUR PHYSICAL BODY SELF TO YOUR DIVINE BODY SELF.

It never stops, does it?

HOW DO YOU FEEL RIGHT NOW?

Peaceful.

WHAT WERE YOU FEELING WHEN WE FIRST BEGAN?

Suffering.

SO, WHAT IS THE "IT" YOU WANT TO STOP?

I guess the quest . . . I just want to be here now!

YOU ARE!

I mean, I just want to feel as if I have completed our destination.

THEN YOU HAVE . . .

Of course, you know I almost died in the river.

THE RIVER IS A GIFTED TEACHER. NOT ONLY DID YOU NOT DIE, YOU WOKE UP ALIVE!

The seeker began to feel like he was dreaming, or lost in some God-based reality show. Did he want to stop now with what he had learned, or take a chance on the next Guide, and hope the lesson did not kill him?
He sat quietly upon the earth, totally present to the moment, and listened for an answer. Soon he began to hear the chanting sound of waves breaking along the seashore. He turned around and stretched out before him, the ocean appeared like a gentle giant of the gods. The blue sea, with all its mystery and

unfathomable depths, drew him closer with its meditative healing song.

He had always loved gazing and meditating to the ocean's mantra. One wave in, one wave out, one wave in, one wave out. This was his special place for times of healing in the past. Sitting, listening, and being . . . Maybe he had already received his gift from the ocean. Maybe not.

WHAT EMOTION DO YOU FEAR THE MOST?

The words startled him. He felt he had been drifting out to sea. He was uncertain. Perhaps anger. Anger seemed to him a plausible and rational answer. None of us likes to feel anger.

WELL, YOU ARE HERE TO FACE YOUR GREATEST FEAR. YOU ARE HERE TO EXPLORE IT, EMBRACE IT, AND LEARN FROM IT. YOU ARE HERE TO DANCE WITH IT!

What are you feeling right now? Remember this is your story as well. What feeling has been the most difficult to understand and to embrace in your life? How often are we so paralyzed by it, that we do everything we can to avoid it, betray it, sabotage it, and destroy it, while never allowing ourselves to penetrate deeply into the very heart of it? How often are we willing to feel every emotion, other than the one we desire and treasure the most? Everything in our world longs for it - the songs we sing, the movies we watch, the books we read - yet we remain so afraid to truly feel it deeply. So afraid . . .

And, then, the strong arms of the sea reached toward the seeker. He felt his heart contract. He gasped, but before he could resist, he was carried into the watery womb. As the ocean pulled him deeper, he felt his body become weightless. He was in a different world. Layers of emotion peeled away and dropped from him, sinking like heavy weights to the ocean floor.

WHAT ARE YOU FEELING RIGHT NOW?

Afraid.

AFRAID OF WHAT?

The unknown. Afraid of being vulnerable. I don't know where I am.

In a sense the seeker felt like a child being rocked by the gentle rhythms of the sea. Anger, sadness, frustrations, loss, and feelings of failure began to disappear. The river had guided him through the fear of change, the fear of pain, and even the fear of dying. Yet, as the ocean brought him deeper and deeper, he felt he was entering into the heart of this enormous sea. And, as paradoxical as it seemed, he sensed that his greatest fear was surfacing within him. He began to cry and the tears tasted just like the salted waters that cradled him. And as he cried, gently rocked within the womb of the sea, he then knew the answer. The ocean is the gift of emotion, and love was the answer to his question. Love was his greatest fear.

But, I do not understand why. We all desire love the most in our lives. How can love be my greatest fear?

YOU DESIRE LOVE ON YOUR TERMS AND CONDITIONS. NOT LOVE AS IT TRULY IS. AS LONG AS YOU TRY TO UNDERSTAND, YOU WILL CONTINUE TO STRUGGLE.

But isn't that why we are here? To attempt to understand the world around us, and the true nature of ourselves?

AS YOU CROSS OVER FROM THE RIVER, THE OCEAN'S GIFT IS FOR YOU TO DISCOVER YOUR TRUE EMOTIONAL SPIRIT. UNDERSTAND THE THINGS IN THIS WORLD MEANT TO BE UNDERSTOOD . . . EXPERIENCE WHAT YOU CANNOT UNDERSTAND.

How do I do that?

YOU ARE DOING IT RIGHT NOW . . . WHY ARE YOU SO AFRAID OF LOVE?

I didn't realize I was.

OF COURSE YOU DID!

As the seeker's body drifted deeper, he could feel his emotional heart opening wider and wider. He realized how willing he was to be unconscious of his feelings, and it was true - he felt afraid of love . . . Of being loved, giving love, receiving love and loving himself.

I don't understand. This should be easy.

IT IS EASY IF YOU STOP TRYING TO UNDERSTAND. YOUR TEARS ARE THE TEARS OF THE OCEAN. THAT IS WHO YOU ARE AND WHERE YOU COME FROM. YOU ARE LOVE. SOMETIMES THAT LOVE IS

EXPRESSED THROUGH SADNESS OR ANGER OR JOY, OR SOMETIMES THROUGH SEX, THROUGH PEACE.

THE OCEAN IS THE MIRROR OF SPIRITUAL LOVE EXPERIENCED IN THE MOMENT. . . NOW.

RIGHT NOW, CRADLED IN THIS WOMB, YOU ARE BEING BORN. LOVE IS BEING BIRTHED.

As he sank deeper into the emerald sea, he felt as if his soul were being bathed in sacred waters, and indeed as if he were being reborn. Layers of his self peeled away, until he was overwhelmed by the grace of unconditional love. This was a love he could not remember ever feeling, as he was rocked in this cradle of salvation. He felt naked, alive, different, so different from whom he thought he was. Life as he knew it seemed like a mirage, an illusion. What he was experiencing now seemed unspeakable, yet so blissful and authentic.

THE FIFTH GIFT
THE WIND
COMMUNICATION OF THE SPIRIT

The playful dance among the leaves

It is the wind

A whisper you can hear in the breeze

It is the wind

A touch upon your face - a gentle kiss

It is the wind

Your heart's song awakening to lover's bliss

It is the wind

Listen to the language of the spirit within

It is the wind

From the depths of the sea, the seeker was gently pulled back and cradled onto a secluded shady beach. He did not know how much time had passed when he again heard the voice.

WHAT DOES IT FEEL LIKE TO BE BORN?

Slowly opening his eyes, the seeker awakened, as if from an enchanted dream. With difficulty, he spoke, "I do not know how to explain it. I feel clean, innocent and nurtured. My life feels new, as if I am now a child who is learning to talk."

THE OCEAN IS A WONDERFUL GUIDE. THE OCEAN IS THE MOTHER OF NATURE'S REBIRTH.

Why do I find it hard to express myself?

LIKE AN INFANT, YOU HAVE MUCH WISDOM, YET WORDS AND FEELINGS ARE BEING NEWLY BIRTHED FROM YOUR HEART. THESE WORDS WILL SPEAK YOUR TRUTH AND YOUR LOVE.

When?

WHEN YOU ARE READY!

Aren't I ready now?

YOU WERE JUST BORN . . . AND LIKE A CHILD, YOU ARE HUNGRY. THAT IS PERFECT. ARE YOU READY?

Yes . . .

LISTEN.

What am I listening for?

JUST LISTEN. IT IS FEEDING TIME.

At that moment, the leaves among the trees began to playfully dance within the invisible moving molecules of air. Seagulls glided effortlessly above the ocean, as the ripples of the surface water sparkled in the sunlight. The chanting wind accentuated the breath of the waves stretching toward the seashore. The cool wind whispered to the surface of his skin, sensuously and gently, until he felt the wind was blowing kisses around his face. Everything lightened up, becoming alive, as the wind orchestrated the most amazing and beautiful symphony. The symphony of nature.

As he breathed deeply, he felt the wind like an invisible angel enter his body. Like an infant being nurtured and fed, he felt himself expand. Instantaneously, he felt connected to every part of his body, and it was at that moment, he felt the spirit of the wind enter his heart.

Wow, I feel funny . . .

IN WHAT WAY?

The space where my heart is feels different. I am seeing and hearing with my heart. I am thinking with my heart, rather than my brain. Yet, it isn't really thinking. It is the feeling of **KNOWING.**

AND WHAT ARE YOU KNOWING?

The grace of love.
The consciousness of communication.
Speaking and listening from the spirit of the heart.

AND HOW WOULD THAT CHANGE YOUR LIFE?

There are so many people in my life I want to share my love with. There are people in my life I want to forgive, and ask forgiveness from. Including myself. There are words I have not shared with others - words of love and acceptance. I just want to share my love, no strings attached, and with no expectations. I want my heart to be open, to be connected to nature in each moment.

As the seeker sat, feeling his heart opening deeper, he also felt the wind's aliveness. The wind was the awakened spirit within him - dancing, leaping, whirling - playing the notes of his heart's emotions while expressing its language through his voice.

What about you? Are you feeling your renewed spirit, and feeling the grace of love in your soul? Are there words and feelings you want to express to people in your life - even to those who are no longer here? What about the people who have judged you, and even hurt you? And what about the people you have judged and hurt? You do not have to think of what to say. When you allow yourself to be guided by nature, when the moment is right, the wind will whisper the words in your ear!

DO YOU THINK YOUR JOURNEY IS OVER?

I believe it is just beginning.

THE WIND HAS FED YOU WELL. YOU ARE GROWING UP.

THE SIXTH GIFT
THE MOUNTAIN
THE GIFT OF WISDOM

Up here in the mountains

The birds fly so high

Clouds surround them

Slowly drifting by

And even if I were alone

I'd love it all

But thank God you're beside me here

So close to my soul

As if he had wings, the wind lifted him upward, and brought him gently down upon a mountain ledge overlooking a panoramic view. He felt peaceful and harmonious as he observed the forest and rivers and streams below. He gazed across the ocean and saw a clear magnificent horizon. What a different perspective of life from up here, he thought.

WELCOME TO THE MOUNTAIN!

I feel very blessed and peaceful up here.

YES, THAT IS TRUE. YOU ARE, AND YOU ALWAYS WERE.

I knew it, but I didn't really know it.
I could see, but I couldn't really see.
I could hear, but I didn't really listen.
I felt, but I really didn't feel.
I thought, but I really didn't experience.

IT IS EASY TO FEEL LOST WHEN YOU FORGET WHO YOU TRULY ARE. FROM THE MOUNTAIN, YOU CAN SEE LIFE AS IT IS . . . NOT WHAT YOU THINK OR WISH IT TO BE.

It is so easy to believe we know, when we really don't. All the books and seminars . . . We begin to live inside the books and seminars, instead of experiencing life itself.

EVERYTHING HAS ITS PURPOSE. THE BOOKS AND SEMINARS ALLOWED THIS JOURNEY TO EVOLVE. THEIR WISDOM LIVES IN YOU AND COMES FORTH TO BE BIRTHED WHEN YOU ALLOW IT.

It is amazing what I can see from here. How can I help others to be guided by the gifts of nature? So many of us struggle and are stuck within our own past, buried beneath the layered soil of our experiences.

BE TRUE TO YOUR OWN SPIRIT AND HEART, AND THE REST WILL FOLLOW. THE MOUNTAIN ALLOWS YOU TO SEE THE WORLD THROUGH THE EYES OF WISDOM. THIS IS THE GIFT OF THE MOUNTAIN - TO BE AN OBSERVER OF LIFE THREE HUNDRED AND SIXTY DEGREES.

At that moment, the seeker closed his eyes and breathed deeply. With his inner knowing, he could see the people down below in the forest searching for answers in their own lives. Some walked steadfastly forward along their path through the woods, making choices they felt would lead to their goals and desires. Others seemed tangled in thick brush and immobilized by fear of the unknown. He saw young people playing in the colorful meadows, their innocent eyes sparkling with passion and joy. He saw the winding steady stream of the river surging forth and could hear the echoes of prayers of those on the shore, too frightened to let go and enter the shifting stream.

He saw others who were lost, but pretending to be content, as they struggled against the tangles of their own beliefs. He turned his inner gaze towards the seashore. There, he saw people who craved love, yet were terrified to open their hearts. So, instead they felt jealousy, fears and control, and called it love.

His heart was uplifted and inspired by those he saw who trusted life, who playfully danced in the fields and surrendered to the river, and who were willing to dive deeply into the abyss of the ocean and explore the depths of joy and love.

He saw a few people who remained peaceful and wise, perched upon the mountains like eagles gazing into the distance. Their meditations radiated light into the valleys below, penetrating into the forests, guiding and assisting others with their healing thoughts and prayers.

At last, he saw himself, searching, waiting and hoping. Yet, strangely, the seeker knew he was observing a reality of himself that no longer existed, but remained like an illusion from his past. Like most human beings, he was trying to find his way.

But, the forest was thick with obstacles, distractions and detours, while from the mountaintop it was easy to see clearly which roads led to freedom, and which led to the feelings of frustration and failure.

WHAT DO YOU SEE?

I see myself, and others, who have felt trapped. I see those who have learned from the gifts of nature, who are not afraid to love and laugh, as well as cry and grieve. I see how easy life can be; yet it is also easy to lose our way and feel lost. Although we have the gift of the mountain-vision, we cannot see from the mountain until we are seeing from the mountain. We must be willing to go within, sit quietly and be lifted up to that perspective. I do not want to lose sight of that!

YOU WILL ALWAYS HAVE YOUR GUIDES. THAT IS WHY THEY EXIST, BUT THERE ARE NO GUARANTEES. YOU DIDN'T THINK YOU WOULD REMAIN ON TOP OF THE MOUNTAIN, DID YOU?

I do not know what to think anymore. I just want to trust the process of living and being.

WELL, YOU HAVE SPENT SO MUCH TIME OBSERVING LIFE BELOW, WHAT DO YOU SEE WHEN YOU LOOK UPWARD?

I see the sky, the clouds, the sun, moon and stars.

WHAT IS IT YOU DON'T SEE?

I don't see what I don't see.
I don't know what I don't know.

YOU HAVE LISTENED TO THE MOUNTAIN WELL!

THE SEVENTH GIFT
THE SKY
THE GIFT OF DIVINE IMAGINATION

We raise our eyes

To heaven's skies

To feel our wings

Hear angels sing

Beyond what we can dream

Nothing is what it seems

Time and space

Holding God's grace

All life divine

The truth we find

Words will disappear

The voice inside becomes so clear

At once, the seeker felt himself flying. Not like some childhood image of superman, but more like traveling through space, effortlessly and instantaneously. He flew past the clouds, beyond the blue sky, amongst the stars and heavens, where bursts of light and color flashed around him.

Do you remember having dreams where you seem to be everywhere, as if time as you understood it no longer existed? Maybe your dream spanned years and when you awoke, you realized you had been asleep for only a brief time. It seemed impossible that your physical body had never left your bed.

The seeker felt as if he too were dreaming, but he was not. At least, not in the way we think of dreams. And although he was still himself, he was no longer the same person who had sat upon the mountain.

Poets, artists, spiritual guides and great sages have all attempted to describe other worlds, heaven and hell, or astral dimensions where archives of past lives are stored, and even the face and presence of God. Metaphors, allegories, music, symbols and parables have all been used to stir and awaken the imaginative spirit in all of us, yet ultimately, the journey is one we must take alone; where sometimes, there are no words to convey the ultimate experience.

I always knew this was possible.
I just did not ***know*** it was possible.

THERE IS ALWAYS THE DIFFERENCE BETWEEN KNOWING WITH UNDERSTANDING AND KNOWING WITH EXPERIENCE.

I still see me sitting on the mountain.

IN A MOMENT YOU WON'T. BUT YOU WILL RETURN TO THE MOUNTAIN AGAIN. RIGHT NOW, YOUR BODY IS RESTING. YOUR PHYSICAL BODY WAS NOT DESIGNED FOR THESE JOURNEYS.

Is this where we go when we die? Is this heaven? I still feel like myself, yet I also feel connected and part of everything.

YOU ARE THE SAME SELF WITHOUT YOUR PHYSICAL BODY AND PHYSICAL CONSCIOUSNESS.

YOUR SPIRIT CONSCIOUSNESS IS PART OF EVERYTHING.

At that moment, the seeker felt so many questions surging through his spirit. Everything he had read and studied about angels, spirits, reincarnation, heaven and people coming back from the other side after near-death experiences were questions he was sincerely hoping to have answered. Questions about Buddha, Mohammed and Christ could now be clarified clearly and directly from God.

HERE'S THE ANSWER TO ALL YOUR QUESTIONS, BECAUSE EVEN HERE IN YOUR SPIRIT CONSCIOUSNESS, THERE IS MEMORY ENCODED LIKE PHYSICAL DUST CLINGING TO YOU. PHYSICAL REALITY IS POWERFUL, AND THE PHYSICAL CONSCIOUS SELF ALWAYS WANTS ANSWERS, AND ALWAYS HAS QUESTIONS. SO HERE ARE THE ANSWERS . . .

THERE IS NO ONE ANSWER TO ANY OF YOUR QUESTIONS!

ALLOW YOUR QUESTIONS TO STIR YOUR IMAGINATION AND TO OPEN YOUR HEART. ALLOW YOUR QUESTIONS TO GUIDE YOU TOWARD POWERFUL EXPERIENCES THAT AWAKEN YOUR SPIRIT. LEARN TO LISTEN AND MEDITATE UPON YOUR QUESTIONS.

EVERYONE WILL UNDERSTAND AND KNOW THE ANSWERS WHEN THEY ARE READY, BUT THE ANSWERS WILL NOT COME FROM A BOOK, OR EVEN THROUGH THE DIVINE MESSAGE OF GOD.

EXPERIENCE WHAT YOU EXPERIENCE
AND *BECOME* THE EXPERIENCE.

EXPERIENCE WHAT YOU EXPERIENCE
AND *LIVE* THE EXPERIENCE.

EXPERIENCE WHAT YOU EXPERIENCE
AND YOU WILL BE *THE EXPERIENCE*.

LIKE A PLANT THAT GENTLY TURNS TOWARDS THE LIGHT, SO IT IS FOR YOU, AND EVERYONE, WHEN YOU ARE READY TO EXPERIENCE THE CONSCIOUSNESS OF SPIRIT THAT LIVES WITHIN YOU AND MOVES YOU TOWARD THE INFINITE GOD CONSCIOUSNESS.

WHEN YOU WERE READY TO BE GUIDED BY THE RIVER, YOU RECEIVED THE RIVER'S WISDOM. WHEN YOU WERE READY TO BE GUIDED BY THE OCEAN, YOUR HEART OPENED AND YOU EXPLORED THE DEPTH OF LOVE.

NOW, YOU ARE READY TO BE A WITNESS TO ALL OF LIFE - HERE AND NOW - FROM PURE CONSCIOUSNESS. THE EXPERIENCE WILL BE A GUIDING FORCE IN YOUR LIFE, AND THEN, YOU WILL RETURN BACK TO YOUR BODY, WITH THE EXPERIENCE OF NATURE'S GIFTS, AND THE GIFT OF THE HUMAN AND DIVINE SPIRIT. EVEN THESE WORDS I SPEAK NOW WILL BE MERELY WORDS LATER, BUT THE EXPERIENCE WILL REMAIN FOREVER.

> *Try to describe love. Regardless of how well you do it, your description will never give the other person YOUR experience of love. And, even when you experience love, who is the YOU that is having the experience?*
>
> *When we are cautious, distrusting and fearful, our experience is different from when we are wise, compassionate and understanding. As we learn and evolve through the gifts of nature, our experience of life becomes clearer, and our experience of love becomes more glorious and extraordinary.*

AS YOU RETURN TO YOUR BODY, AND AS YOU RETURN TO THE LIFE YOU LIVE, CONTINUE TO BE GUIDED BY THE GIFTS OF NATURE THAT SURROUND YOU. REMEMBER WHAT EACH OF NATURE'S GIFTS OFFERED YOU, AND EACH DAY *BE THE EXPERIENCE.* HONOR YOUR LESSONS AND HONOR YOUR CHALLENGES.

It is impossible to share these experiences with others, isn't it? They must be experienced by each of us. Even if I try to tell others what I have seen, the words will sound clichéd. I understand why you say we must BE the experience. That is my everyday challenge, isn't it?

ULTIMATELY THAT IS WHY YOU ARE HERE. YOU UNDERSTOOD THIS BEFORE.

NOW, YOU KNOW - *TRULY KNOW!*

How will this affect my life?

YOU ALREADY KNOW THE ANSWERS TO YOUR QUESTIONS, BUT I KNOW YOU LOVE TO ASK THEM . . . SO FOR NOW, I'LL GIVE YOU THE ANSWER: YES!

The seeker began to laugh - laughter, as if he had never laughed before. He felt the heavens shake and the stars dance, as his laughter echoed across the ripples of space. He realized how much he had missed the joy from laughter, and the simple pleasures of being alive. He had often imagined that God would have a sense of humor. Why else would we laugh?

NOW YOU WILL DISCOVER MORE LAUGHTER IN YOUR LIFE.

At that moment, the seeker looked down and once again saw his body. *Will I remember everything?* he thought.

THIS IS NOT A DREAM. YOU WILL REMEMBER EVERYTHING!

Will I continue to hear your voice?

WHEN YOU LISTEN, YOU WILL ALWAYS HEAR MY VOICE. YOUR GUIDES ARE ALL AROUND YOU.

It seemed as if his body had sat patiently waiting for him to arrive, and then in a flash, he did. He was back, facing the morning sun. The warm rays felt delicious on his face, as if he could lick his lips and taste the light. The gentle coolness of the air penetrated deeply into his body. He had been reborn, renewed and felt miraculously alive. It seemed like only a moment ago that he had been suffering and had asked for guidance, and now he felt joy and peacefulness. It was hard to believe what he had just experienced, and yet it was true, he did remember everything!
He could still see the flowers in the field and hear the wind laughing, yes laughing, between the blades of grass.

The time is NOW! Now is the time, he thought. And, then he heard voices.

"Dad, where have you been? We've been looking all over for you."

The seeker smiled at his beloved children. "I've been right here all along."

"You weren't here a few minutes ago."

"Well, I was meditating and asking for guidance . . . when,"

"Dad, I'm sorry to interrupt you, but can you tell us the rest of the story at the beach? We have only one more day to swim in the ocean."

"By the ocean would be the perfect place to share the rest of the story. It would be my heart's desire."

At that moment, he felt his creative spirit prompt his imagination . . . and, he thought, maybe I will even share this experience with everyone.

And, that is what he did.

He traveled through space and time
Pure spirit and conscious mind
Beyond what he could conceive
Beyond what he could believe

Experienced colors never seen
Experienced the inside-out of dreams
Where thought with the speed of light
Entered worlds beyond day and night

Mysteries revealed and so much more
In ways he'd never imagined before
Yes, what you've heard is true
The Spirit of God lives inside of you

REFLECTIONS

As you have journeyed through this story, can you feel your own creative spirit awakening? Are you ready now to be in your life with a renewed passion? Can you hear the voice of nature speaking to you, and inviting you to experience this life fully?

Even with the daily stresses that surround you, can you now feel the blessings that live inside you? How would your life change if each day you embraced the gifts that nature generously gives? The earth, the trees and flowers, the flowing streams, the ocean, the wind, the mountain and the sky have always been guides to teach you.

As we listen closely, these gifts can transform our lives daily.

The time is **NOW** . . .

GUIDED QUESTIONS

1. EARTH - BELIEFS

What beliefs about yourself have interfered with your full expression of creativity, joy and love in your life?

What beliefs have empowered your creative spirit to pursue your dreams in all areas of your life?

What beliefs would you like to create now in your life?

2. SEEDS - CREATION

How have you been creative in your life?

How do you feel about yourself when you are creative?

If time and money were not an obstacle in your life, what would you love to learn, or do, or create?

3. RIVER - CHANGE

What fears do you feel when you think about changing something in your life?

Imagine what your life would be like if you felt the freedom to let go of those fears and reconnect to your divine power?

What would be different in your life?

4. OCEAN - EMOTION

What painful experiences from the past keep you from trusting your heart?

Are there areas of your life where you are making yourself wrong?

What are you still judging someone else for?

What are your fears of opening your heart and receiving and giving the gift of love?

Imagine forgiving yourself and others for everything and feeling the healing power of love. How would that change your life?

5. WIND - SPIRIT'S COMMUNICATION

As you open your heart to forgiveness and compassion, who can you now share this gift with without expectations?

Describe the qualities you are choosing to have present in all your relationships.

6. MOUNTAIN - WISDOM

What goals from your past have you accomplished?

What are five things you appreciate about yourself?

What new visions can you now see in the distance?

What specific actions do you see yourself taking to fulfill these visions?

7. SKY - DIVINE IMAGINATION

Close your eyes and imagine your life surrounded by peace, joy, abundance and love. Imagine this peace and love surrounding the planet earth and bringing healing to each person living here. Imagine a world where this is possible. Imagine who you are as you bring these divine gifts by your thoughts and actions to everyone and everything.

THE GIFTS FROM NATURE ALIGN WITH THE CHAKRAS IN OUR BODIES

The chakras are seven subtle energy centers located in specific areas of the body. They are associated with particular qualities, functions and feelings. They work on several levels of our life: the physical, the emotional and the spiritual. Our life force or *prana* flows through these areas, though at times this life force can be obstructed by physical or emotional ailments or imbalances.

THE EARTH - FIRST CHAKRA - RED

Located at the base of the spine, this is the foundation of the body and the physical base of ***unconscious energy and memory***.

THE SEED - SECOND CHAKRA - ORANGE

This chakra is located over the spleen and genital area. This area ***influences the subconscious energy*** of the creative force.

THE RIVER - THIRD CHAKRA - YELLOW

Located behind the navel, this chakra is the ***bridge between intellectual and emotional security***, and letting go of false beliefs and fears.

THE OCEAN - FOURTH CHAKRA - GREEN

In the center of the chest located around the heart, this chakra ***governs awakening to compassion, forgiveness and love***.

THE WIND - FIFTH CHAKRA - BLUE

Located around and in the throat, this chakra ***enables clear emotions and thoughts to be expressed through our voice***.

THE MOUNTAIN - SIXTH CHAKRA - WHITE

Located between the eyebrows, pineal gland, here is the ***seat of intuition and spiritual wisdom***.

THE SKY - SEVENTH CHAKRA - VIOLET

At the crown of the head, here is our strongest connection to pure consciousness, enlightenment, and ***Oneness with God Consciousness***.

GUIDED MEDITATION

Close your eyes and sit comfortably. As you relax, feel the foundation of your earth at the base of your spine. Allow yourself to experience the source of your power revitalizing the very soil in your soul. Visualize the color red with all its energy moving upward through your spine and into your body. Begin to feel the seed of the second chakra blossoming with its creative force. Observe the area of the genitalia being awakened with expressed joy and life as the color orange radiates within you.

Relaxing deeper, begin to feel the current of the river as you focus on your abdominal area of the third chakra. See the brightness of yellow expanding, wanting to free you from your past, and begin to discover the power of NOW as you release all your false beliefs and fears.

Breathe deeply and slowly and begin to feel a profound peacefulness as your spirit moves into your heart where the healing color of green is in the fourth chakra. Feel yourself bathed in the womb of the ocean as your heart opens to the greatest gift of love. Feel that love expanding and reaching out with compassion and forgiveness, healing yourself and others with each breath of life.

Experience that love as it moves into your throat and the fifth chakra opens your voice. Feel the freedom of the wind dancing in the aura of a blue light throughout your body, effortlessly and joyfully. Allow yourself to experience this beautiful gift of the wind.

As you relax deeper, feel the blue light carry you higher. See yourself on top of the mountain in the sixth chakra, as your gaze relaxes through your pineal gland between your eyebrows. A white light surrounds everything as you easily scan the world we live in, bringing healing and peace with each breath and thought. You feel one with the design of life, connected and whole, guided with spiritual wisdom.

And then you look upward toward the crown of your head, the seventh chakra, where a violet aura spontaneously frees you from your body, and you are with the gift of the sky and the heavens. Allow yourself to experience what is beyond your understanding or imagination. Allow yourself to experience the consciousness of God and the sacredness of Divine Aliveness. Breathe and experience.

As you return to your body, and as you return to the life you live, continue to be guided by the gifts in nature that surround you and also come from within your own being.

Remember what each of nature's gifts offered you, and each day ***BE*** the experience. Honor your lessons and honor your challenges.

ABOUT DR. MARTY FINKELSTEIN

Dr. Marty Finkelstein has been a holistic chiropractor since 1980 specializing in physical, emotional, and spiritual well being. He has hosted "To Your Health", a cable television show, and "Wake Up To Your Health", an Atlanta radio show.

He has been a chiropractic representative for Flying Doctors Of America, where he has teamed with medical doctors, dentists, and other health care professionals providing services to thousands of people in Mexico, Peru, and The Dominican Republic.

Dr. Finkelstein is the author of:

A Life Of Wellness, guidelines for avoiding illness

8 Lessons For Life On Hole 1, a story about a young boy who learns valuable lessons of life playing the game of golf

If Relationships Were Like Sports, Men Would At Least Know The Score, empowering the romance and intimacy of relationships

Divorce…An Uncommon Love Story, how to heal your family, save your money, and renew your life

Moments In Time – a CD of 15 original songs

Dr. Marty Finkelstein has a holistic chiropractic office in Decatur, and Conyers Georgia

To order additional copies of THE SEVEN GIFTS
as well as any other books......

Write to:

Dr. Marty Finkelstein
4292 D Memorial drive
Decatur, Georgia, 30032

Or E-Mail - drmarty3@yahoo.com
www.mydecaturchiropractor.com

Dr. Marty Finkelstein is available for speaking engagements, as well as leading wellness and healing workshops.

LaVergne, TN USA
05 December 2010
207456LV00002B/1/P